KU-443-052

MEDITATION
COLOURING BOOK

MEDITATION
COLOURING BOOK
Wonderful images to melt your worries away

ARCTURUS

ARCTURUS

This edition published in 2015 by Arcturus Publishing Limited
26/27 Bickels Yard, 151–153 Bermondsey Street,
London SE1 3HA

Copyright © Arcturus Holdings Limited

All rights reserved. No part of this publication may be reproduced,
stored in a retrieval system, or transmitted, in any form or by any means,
electronic, mechanical, photocopying, recording or otherwise, without
prior written permission in accordance with the provisions of the
Copyright Act 1956 (as amended). Any person or persons who do any
unauthorised act in relation to this publication may be liable to criminal
prosecution and civil claims for damages.

ISBN: 978-1-78404-632-3
AD004597NT

Printed in Spain

Introduction

Colouring is a useful relaxation technique which helps you enter a freer state of being. *The Meditation Colouring Book* contains a mass of mandalas and other abstract images to soothe the mind and please the senses. It is designed to take you to that peaceful place where meditation can occur.

Mandalas are 'sacred circles', geometric shapes without a beginning or an end. They echo the balance and symmetry of the world around us – from the nucleus of a cell to the structure of a snowflake – and they symbolize harmony, wholeness and healing.

By colouring in these designs you will de-stress your mind and body and create your own beautiful artworks. So put your worries on hold, pick up your crayons, pencils or felt-tips, and let zen be your guide . . .

relax and Meditate